La Pluche

La

Pluche

by Camille Sokol

and drawing by Bill Sokol

Holt, Rinehart and Winston • New York / Chicago / San Francisco

For...Aurore, *Barbara, Claire, David, Eileen, Frances, Georges,* Honoré, *Irma, Jack, Kathy, Lindsay, Maida, Nick, Olive, Pierre, Quintina, Randy, Suzanne, Taubie, Ubert, Velvull, Willy, Xylia, Yollande, Zay.*

La Pluche a une femme et trois enfants. Non, il en a quatre.
Un, deux, trois, quatre.

La Pluche has a wife and three children. No, he has four.
One, two, three, four.

La Pluche, est-ce que c'est une maison?
Oui, je crois que c'est une maison.

La Pluche, is this a house?
Yes, I believe it is a house.

Et cela, La Pluche, est-ce que c'est une auto?
Ah, oui, ça c'est une auto.

And is that a car, La Pluche?
Oh, yes, that is a car.

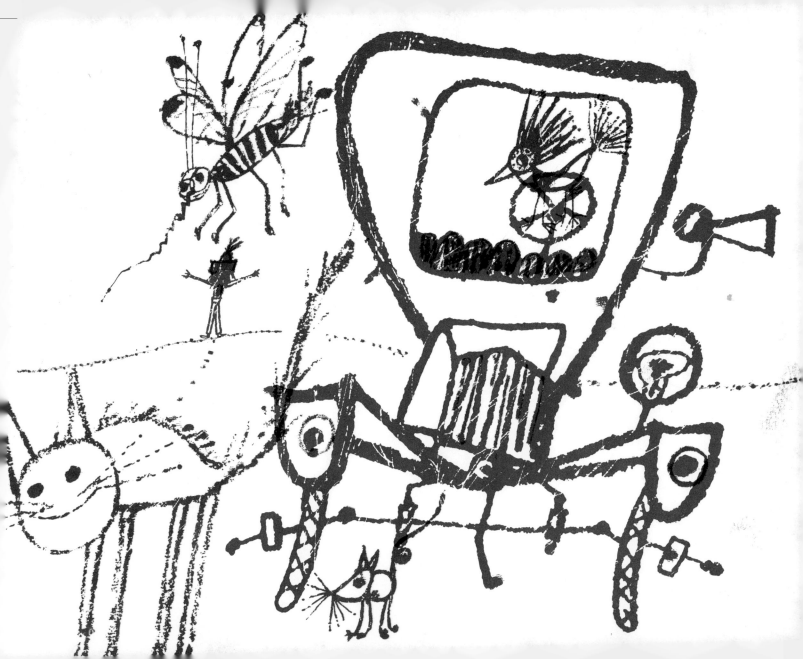

La Pluche, est-ce que tu es assis?
Je ne suis pas assis; je suis étendu parmi les fleurs.

La Pluche, are you sitting?
I am not sitting; I am resting among the flowers.

La Pluche, regarde cela! C'est une chaise!
Oui, c'est une chaise, mais cela, c'est une table.

La Pluche, look at that! It's a chair!
Yes, it is a chair, but that's a table.

La Pluche, nous n'avons pas de vêtements!
Non, mais nous avons des cintres.

La Pluche, we have no clothes!
No, but we have clothes hangers.

La Pluche, est-ce que c'est un poêle?
Oui, c'est un poêle, mais il faut aussi du bois
et peut-être un poisson ou deux.

La Pluche, is that a stove?
Yes, that is a stove, but you also need some wood
and perhaps a fish or two.

La Pluche, fais attention! Il n'y a pas de marches!
Oui, il y a des marches. Voilà les marches!

La Pluche, be careful, there are no steps!
Yes, there are steps. *There* are the steps!

La Pluche! Est-ce qu'il y a quelque chose dans l'arbre?
Non, il n'y a rien dans l'arbre.

La Pluche! Is there something in the tree?
No, there is nothing in the tree.

Et sur la clôture, qu'est-ce que c'est que ça?
C'est un oiseau à deux pattes.

And what is that on the fence?
That is a bird with two legs.

La Pluche, qu'est-ce qu'il y a dans le ciel?
Le soleil, un nuage, et une mouche.

La Pluche, what is in the sky?
The sun, one cloud, and one fly.

Regarde par terre, La Pluche! C'est un serpent dangereux!
Mais non, c'est seulement un petit ver qui travaille dans la terre.

Look on the ground, La Pluche! There is a dangerous snake!
Why no, it is only a little worm who is working in the ground.

La Pluche, est-ce que c'est un bateau?
Oui, c'est un bateau.

La Pluche, is that a boat?
Yes, that is a boat.

Et est-ce que ce sont des poissons?
Oui, ce sont des poissons.

And, are those fish?
Yes, those are fish.

La Pluche, nous avons cinq enfants!
Non, nous en avons quatre. Un, deux, trois, quatre, et ça, c'est un lion.

La Pluche, we have five children!
No, we have four. One, two, three, four, and *that* is a lion.

La Pluche, qui est là-bas?
Là-bas? C'est, ma femme, c'est une bonne question.

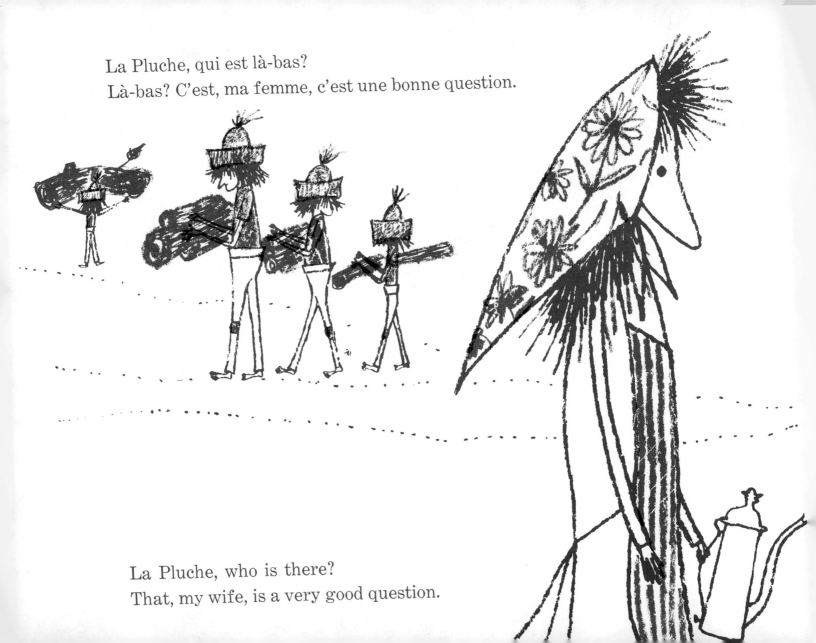

La Pluche, who is there?
That, my wife, is a very good question.

About the Author and Artist

Camille and Bill Sokol, unlike the
La Pluche family, have two daughters
and one—no two—cats!

Writing in both French and English
comes naturally to Mrs. Sokol, who grew
up in a bilingual home in Montreal.
She recalls being fascinated
as a child by an utterly shiftless,
lackadaisical fellow, a soft-
hearted wanderer who was blissfully
unaware of his own lack of
material goods. His resilient charm
was the original inspiration
for the character of La Pluche.

Mr. Sokol, a man of parts, is frequently
called "Luther Burbank" by his
family, because of the hours he spends
devising ingenious ways to make
his plants grow. An Art Director for
The New York Times, he has
illustrated numerous books for children
and has received citations from
the AIGA, Art Director's Club of New
York, and *Graphis* Magazine.